**Oxford Read and Imagine**

1

# On Thin Ice

By Paul Shipton

Illustrated by Fabiano Fiorin

Activities by Hannah Fish

## Contents

**OXFORD**

UNIVERSITY PRESS

2

Ben
Rosie's brother

Rosie
Ben's sister

Grandpa

Clunk
Grandpa's robot

Mom

Now let's read this story,
On Thin Ice!

'It's hot today, Grandpa,' says Rosie.
'Why are you wearing a big coat
and boots?'

Grandpa smiles and says, 'It's hot here,
but I'm going to a very cold place ...'

'Can I come?' asks Ben.

'Me, too!' says Rosie.

'Yes,' says Grandpa. 'Look! Clunk has big coats and boots for you, too.'

Soon they are in the van.

'Let's go, Clunk!' says Grandpa. 'I'm too hot in this coat!'

→ Go to page 20 for activities.

The van stops in a new place. It is very white and very cold.

'Where are we?' asks Rosie.

'We're in the Arctic!' says Grandpa.

Ben is pointing at the sea. 'Look!' he says. 'There are seals in the water.'

'And look there,' says Grandpa. 'I can see two young polar bears on the ice.'

'Are they fighting?' asks Ben.

'No,' says Grandpa. 'They're playing. They're little cubs.'

'I like them!' says Rosie. 'Can we go close to them?'

I like them!

Go to page 21 for activities.

'No, don't go close,' says Grandpa.
'I can't see their mother, but big polar
   bears are dangerous.'

'Where is the mother now?' asks Ben.

'She's finding food for her cubs,' says
Grandpa. He points at the sea. 'Polar
bears eat seals.'

Where is the mother now?

The two cubs stop their game.
They look up and see the children.

'They're scared of us,' says Ben.

'Don't be scared!' Clunk shouts
to the cubs.

But one of the cubs runs.

→ Go to page 22 for activities.

There is a new sound from the ice, and the cub stops.

'Oh no!' says Grandpa. 'The ice is too thin there. The cub can't walk on it!'

There are cracks in the ice under the cub's feet.

Soon the cracks in the ice are big. The cub is very scared.

'He can't swim,' says Grandpa. 'He's too young.'

Clunk goes on the ice, but he soon stops. 'I'm sorry,' he says. 'The ice is too thin for me, too.'

He can't swim.

→ Go to page 23 for activities.

'Grandpa, look!' shouts Ben.

A big polar bear is running on the ice. She is the cubs' mother!

'Quick, go to the van!' says Grandpa. 'The mother wants to protect her cubs!'

The mother bear goes to the thin ice.

'It's too thin for a big bear!' says Rosie.

But the mother bear lies down on the ice. Then she crawls to the scared cub.

'Polar bears can't walk on thin ice, but they can crawl,' says Grandpa.

→ Go to page 24 for activities.

The little cub is scared, but he watches his mother. Then he lies down and crawls on the ice, too.

'Look!' says Ben. 'The cub is learning from his mother. That's fantastic!'

Soon the cub is on thick ice.

That's fantastic!

Then the mother bear turns and looks at Grandpa, Ben, and Rosie. She stands up on two legs and roars.

'Now she's angry,' says Grandpa. 'She wants to protect her cubs. RUN!'

→ Go to page 25 for activities.

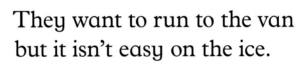

They want to run to the van but it isn't easy on the ice.

Ben looks at the cubs' mother. With her big feet, she is very quick on the ice.

'I have an idea!' says Rosie.

I have an idea!

'We can't run, but we can slide,' says Rosie. 'Watch me!'

She slides on the ice.

Ben, Clunk, and Grandpa slide, too, and soon they are at the van.

'Let's go home!' says Ben.

→ Go to page 26 for activities.

The mother bear is running at the van.

'Quick, Clunk!' says Grandpa.

The mother bear is very close.
She jumps at the van ...

But now there is no van! There are
no people.

The mother bear walks to her cubs.

At home, Mom sees Ben and Rosie.

'Take off those big coats and boots!
And wash your hands for dinner,
please,' Mom says.

Grandpa smiles. 'Your mom is
protecting HER children!' he says.

→ Go to page 27 for activities.

##  Activities for pages 4–5

**1 Put a tick (✓) or a cross (✗) in the box.**

**1** This is a coat.  ✗

**2** This is cold. ☐

**3** This is hot. ☐

**4** These are boots. ☐

**2 Write *yes* or *no*.**

**1** It is a cold day.  _no_

**2** Grandpa is wearing a coat and boots.  _____

**3** Grandpa is going to a hot place.  _____

**4** Ben and Rosie can go with Grandpa.  _____

**5** Clunk has hats for the children.  _____

**Activities** for pages 6–7

## 1 Write the words.

**1** o l d c

cold

**2** o a r l p e r a b

_____

**3** g t h f i

_____

**4** a e s

_____

**5** l p c e a

_____

**6** e a s l

_____

**7** t r A c i c

_____

**8** b u c

_____

**9** c e i

_____

**Talk** **Do you like seals? Do you like polar bears? Talk to a friend.**

# Activities for pages 8–9

**1 Choose and write the correct words.**

Grandpa can't see the ¹ <u>mother</u> polar
bear. She is finding food for her cubs. The cubs
stop their ² _____ and look at the van.
They are ³ _____. One of the cubs
⁴ _____.

runs    ~~mother~~    game    close    scared

**2 Match.**

| | |
|---|---|
| 1 Big polar bears | eat seals. |
| 2 Polar bears | are scared. |
| 3 The cubs stop | their game. |
| 4 They see | are dangerous. |
| 5 The cubs | the children. |
| 6 Clunk shouts | to the cubs. |

**Activities** for pages 10–11

## 1 Order the words.

**1** sound / the ice. / There is / from / a new

_There is a new sound from the ice._

**2** too thin / there. / The / is / ice

_____

**3** cub's feet. / are / There / under / cracks / the

_____

**4** is / swim. / The cub / too young / to

_____

## 2 Look at the picture on page 10. Answer the questions.

**1** How many children are there?     two

**2** How many polar bears
are there?                    _____

**3** What color are the cubs?      _____

**4** Where is Clunk?        next to _____

**5** What color is the van?        _____

                         and white.

**6** What is Grandpa looking at? the _____

## Activities for pages 12–13

**1** **Write the words.**

1 ___quick___  k i c q u

2 _____  w a c l r

3 _____  i e l w n o d

4 _____  c t e p o r t

**2** **Complete the sentences.**

> lies down  crawls  walk
> running  ~~shouts~~

1 Ben __shouts__ to Grandpa.

2 The mother polar bear is _____.

3 The mother polar bear _____ on the ice.

4 She _____ to her cub.

5 Polar bears can't _____ on thin ice.

## 1 Circle the correct words.

1 The cub **watch** / **watches** his mother.

2 The cub lies down and crawls, **too** / **to**.

3 The cub is **learning** / **learn** from his mother.

4 Soon the cub is **no** / **not** on thin ice.

5 Then the mother polar bear **turning** / **turns**.

6 She looks **at** / **of** Grandpa, Ben, and Rosie.

7 The mother polar bear stands up **on** / **at** two legs and roars.

## 2 Match.

| | |
|---|---|
| 1 The mother polar | roars! |
| 2 She stands up | protect her cubs. |
| 3 Then she | the children to run. |
| 4 The big polar bear | on two legs. |
| 5 She wants to | bear turns. |
| 6 Grandpa tells | is angry. |

**Talk** **Do Grandpa and the children get away? Tell a friend your ideas.**

## 1 Choose and write the correct words.

They want to ¹ _____ to the van but
it isn't easy on the ice. Then Rosie has an
² _____. She slides on the ³ _____.
Ben and Grandpa ⁴ _____ too, and soon
they are at the van.

ice    run    learn    slide    idea

## 2 Look at the picture on page 17. Write *yes* or *no*.

1 Rosie is sliding on the ice. _____

2 Ben is next to Rosie. _____

3 Clunk is helping Grandpa. _____

4 There are two polar bears. _____

5 The mother polar bear is roaring. _____

**Activities** for pages 18–19

## 1 Order the words.

**1** runs / the / The / van. / mother bear / at

_____

**2** Then / at / the van. / jumps / she

_____

**3** there / no van. / But / is / now

_____

## 2 Put a tick (✓) or a cross (✗) in the box.

**1** This is smile. ☐

**2** These are people. ☐

**3** This is a crack. ☐

**4** These are children. ☐

**Talk** **Do you like this story? Talk to a friend.**

# Animals in Cold Places

**1** **This story is about polar bears. What did you find out about them? Draw a picture of a polar bear and answer the questions.**

Where do polar bears live?

Polar bears live in the Arctic.

What do they eat?

What color are they?

What is the name for a baby polar bear?

**Talk** **Do you know more about polar bears? Talk to a friend.**

**2** **Now find out about seals. Draw a picture of a seal and answer the questions.**

Where do seals live?

What do they eat?

What color are they?

What is the name for a baby seal?

How do seals stay warm?

What animals eat seals?

**Talk** **What other animals live in cold places? Talk to a friend.**

# Picture Dictionary

angry    Arctic    boots    close

  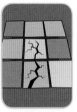 

coat    cold    crack    crawl

cub    dangerous    fight    game

hot    ice    learn    lie down

mother

place

polar bear

protect

quick

roar

run

sea

seal

shout

slide

smile

sound

thick

thin

turn

# Oxford Read and Imagine

**Oxford Read and Imagine** graded readers are at nine levels (Early Starter, Starter, Beginner, and Levels 1 to 6) for students from age 3 to 4 and older. They offer great stories to read and enjoy.

Activities provide Cambridge Young Learner Exams preparation. See Key below.

At Levels 1 to 6, every storybook reader links to an **Oxford Read and Discover** non-fiction reader, giving students a chance to find out more about the world around them, and an opportunity for Content and Language Integrated Learning (CLIL).

For more information about **Read and Imagine**, and for Teacher's Notes, go to www.oup.com/elt/teacher/readandimagine

**KEY**  Activity supports Cambridge Young Learner Starters Exam preparation

 **Oxford Read and Discover**

Do you want to find out more about young animals? You can read this non-fiction book.

## OXFORD
UNIVERSITY PRESS

Great Clarendon Street, Oxford, OX2 6DP, United Kingdom

Oxford University Press is a department of the University of Oxford. It furthers the University's objective of excellence in research, scholarship, and education by publishing worldwide. Oxford is a registered trade mark of Oxford University Press in the UK and in certain other countries

© Oxford University Press 2016

The moral rights of the author have been asserted

First published in 2016

2023

12

ISBN: 978 0 19 470931 6

Printed in China

This book is printed on paper from certified and well-managed sources

ACKNOWLEDGEMENTS

*Main illustrations by*: Fabiano Fiorin/ Milan Illustrations Agency.

*Additional illustrations by*: Dusan Pavlic/ Beehive illustration, Alan Rowe, Mark Ruffle.